DISC...

PLANET SOS

CHANGING CLIMATE

Gerry Bailey

Gareth Stevens
Publishing

Please visit our Web site, www.garethstevens.com. For a free color catalog of all our high-quality books, call toll free 1-800-542-2595 or fax 1-877-542-2596.

Library of Congress Cataloging-in-Publication Data

Bailey, Gerry.
 Changing climate / Gerry Bailey.
     p. cm. — (Planet SOS)
 Includes index.
 ISBN 978-1-4339-4962-3 (library binding)
 ISBN 978-1-4339-4963-0 (pbk.)
 ISBN 978-1-4339-4964-7 (6-pack)
 1. Climatic changes. 2. Global environmental change. I. Title.
 QC903.B16 2011
 551.6—dc22

                                        2010032885

Published in 2011 by
Gareth Stevens Publishing
111 East 14th Street, Suite 349
New York, NY 10003

Designer: Simon Webb
Editor: Felicia Law

Printed in the United States of America

CPSIA compliance information: Batch #CW11GS: For further information contact Gareth Stevens, New York, New York at 1-800-542-2595.

CONTENTS

WHAT IS CLIMATE?

Depending on where you live, you'll get different kinds of weather at varying times of the year. In some places the differences are quite large. There might be a long period of cold during the winter months, with snow and ice, followed by a warm summer. There are places with rainy seasons and others that have long periods of drought, where there's no rain at all. But all of these weather patterns tend to remain similar from one year to the next. The kind of weather you experience over a long period of time is called climate.

What makes climate

Temperature

The sun heats Earth's atmosphere as well as its seas. But because Earth tilts and spins on its axis, as well as moving in an orbit around the sun, different regions are heated at different times, creating various climates.

Water vapor

Water vapor is a gas made up of tiny droplets of water that hang in the air. The amount of water vapor in the air is called its humidity. Humidity can determine the amount of rain an area receives.

Ocean currents

The heating and cooling of the oceans causes large movements of water called currents. Currents that flow from near the equator are warm. Those from the poles are cold. Currents can warm or cool the atmosphere, causing a particular climate.

Prevailing winds

Winds are movements of Earth's atmosphere and tend to blow in the same direction at the same time of the year. Prevailing winds – those that blow most often – affect ocean currents.

Pressure

The weight of the air in our atmosphere is always pressing down on Earth's surface. This is called air pressure, or atmospheric pressure. The warmer the air, the lighter it is. Differences in air pressure between areas can cause winds to blow between them.

Distance from the sea

Lands that are far from the sea have a greater temperature range than those close to it. This is because the land heats up more quickly than the sea.

Our spinning globe reacts to the gravitational pull of the moon. This pull affects the movement of ocean waters and air.

Remote weather stations like this provide regular information.

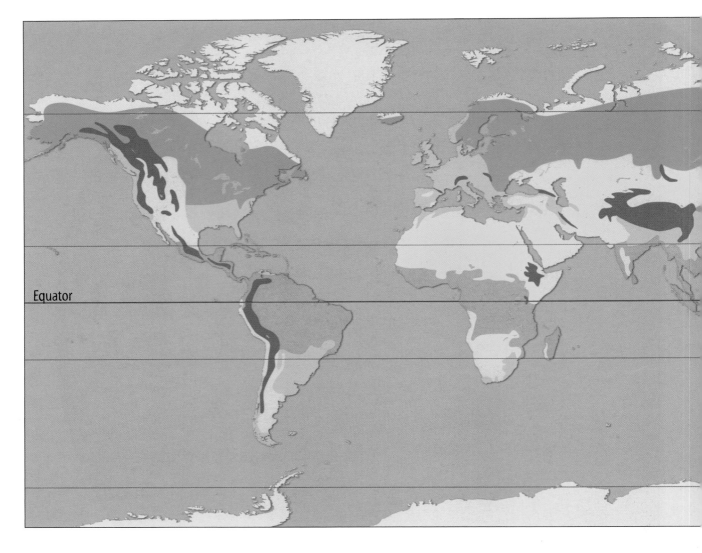

Equator

World climates

Climate tells you the kind of weather you would expect to find in a region of the world during a certain part of the year. Different parts of the globe experience different patterns of climate. They are called climate zones.

The map shows the main types of climate around the world.

POLAR – extremely cold and dry. Often covered in ice for most of the year.

CONTINENTAL – summers can be cool to hot, winters are long and cold.

MOUNTAIN – cold all year at the mountain peaks, but warmer lower down.

El Niño

El Niño is part of a weather cycle that affects the Pacific Ocean every few years. Usually, the winds blow from east to west and push warm water with them. But when El Niño sets in, the winds drop, or even reverse direction. El Niño seems to have been strengthening in recent years, causing droughts in Indonesia, southeast Africa, South America and Australia.

This satellite chart shows some unusual red and white areas. These are warm waters that have been pushed from the western Pacific to the eastern Pacific by El Niño. Normally these waters would be cold.

NORTH AMERICA

PACIFIC OCEAN

TEMPERATE – winters are cold or cool while summers are warm. Rain all year round.

TROPICAL – hot and wet all year round; some regions are dry with a wet season known as a monsoon.

ARID – dry all year round, as in deserts.

El Niño is one cause of the destruction of the coral reefs. These are home to many plants and fish, but the rise in the temperature of the sea destroys the algae that protect the reef. The coral turns white and dies.

Weather cycles

Our climate is made up of cycles of weather. This means that the weather changes over a period of time in patterns that repeat themselves and are known as seasons.

Earth travels around the sun once a year and, as it does, the amount of sunlight that shines on different parts of Earth's surface varies. This gives us the different seasons. Heat from the sun makes water and air expand and move around. These movements in the atmosphere and the oceans bring about the weather cycles.

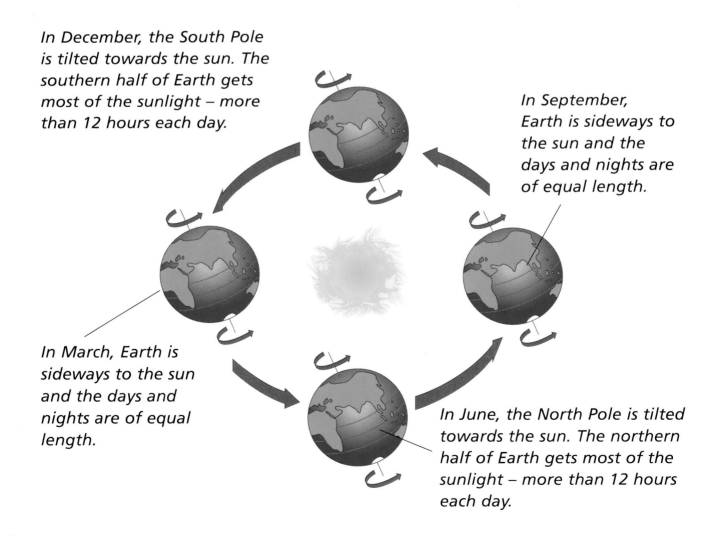

In December, the South Pole is tilted towards the sun. The southern half of Earth gets most of the sunlight – more than 12 hours each day.

In September, Earth is sideways to the sun and the days and nights are of equal length.

In March, Earth is sideways to the sun and the days and nights are of equal length.

In June, the North Pole is tilted towards the sun. The northern half of Earth gets most of the sunlight – more than 12 hours each day.

Weather trackers

In 1959, NASA launched Vanguard II, which sent back the first photographs from space of Earth's cloud cover. The next year TIROS was launched. It showed that satellites could observe Earth's weather patterns.

From then on, satellites have given a detailed picture of moisture, rainfall and cloud cover as well as measuring winds.

Some satellites follow an orbit over the poles.

Metop-A is part of a joint US–European satellite program.

HOT AND GASSY

During the billions of years that Earth has existed, its climate has changed from time to time. There has always been global warming and global cooling. So why are we so worried now? For the first time, it seems that global warming is happening because of what HUMANS are doing.

There are many natural reasons for climate change. Earth may not receive the same amount of heat and light from the sun, or there may be a change to its orbit. Very large-scale volcanic eruptions can alter climate as well – gases from the volcano rise high into the atmosphere and cool, forming layers of droplets that bounce the sun's rays back into space.

Burning coal releases the greenhouse gas carbon dioxide into the air.

Many smaller ski resorts are closing as each year less and less snow falls on the slopes.

The greenhouse effect

When gardeners want to help plants grow they might put them in a glass construction called a greenhouse. The greenhouse traps the heat from the sun rather than letting it escape into the atmosphere.

When gases such as carbon dioxide or methane are present in the air they cause our atmosphere to act as a giant greenhouse, trapping the sun's heat that would normally escape into space. Normally we need a certain amount of these gases to keep the planet warm enough to sustain life. Unfortunately, too much gas in the atmosphere will cause Earth to overheat and bring danger to all living things.

People are exposed to dangerous rays from the sun as Earth's protective atmosphere changes.

A problem gas

When we think of greenhouse gas, we tend to think of carbon dioxide. This is the gas we usually blame when we talk about global warming. But there is another greenhouse gas that's actually even more dangerous: methane.

Scientists have worked out that the amount of methane in our atmosphere has more than doubled since 1800. That's a lot, because methane is calculated to be around 23 times more powerful than carbon dioxide at trapping heat that would otherwise escape into space.

Amazingly, tiny termites, such as those that live in these high mounds, release 5 percent of total global emissions of methane. That small percentage is about 5.5 million tons (5 million metric tons).

Ground layers of permafrost start to thaw.

Permafrost

Methane can seep into Earth's atmosphere from landfills, coal mines and leaking gas pipes. One source that has many scientists worried is the methane buried in the permafrost. Permafrost is the layer of rock and soil in cold areas that remains permanently frozen. As the permafrost melts with global warming, bacteria that were trapped in the ice are released and produce methane. Even a small melt of permafrost could have a big impact on Earth's atmosphere.

Cows and sheep digest food in such a way that they expel large quantities of methane.

The lungs of the planet

Rainforests are found in hot tropical regions. Once they covered 14 percent of Earth's surface. Now they cover just 6 percent. The cutting down, or deforestation, of the rainforests is a threat not just to the people and animals that live in it but to us all. When plants breathe in, they absorb dangerous carbon dioxide, and when they breathe out they give off oxygen, which we and other animals need to breathe.

The rainforest is home to millions of different species of plants and animals.

Rainforests help to reduce the effects of greenhouse gases in Earth's atmosphere. The huge Amazon forest of Brazil alone produces 20 percent of Earth's oxygen.

Years of forest clearance have removed huge areas of the Amazon rainforest. Logging destroys 2.5 acres (1 ha) of this forest every minute or two. At this rate, the rainforests may no longer exist in just 50 years' time.

THE AMAZON RAINFOREST

AREA Approximately 2.5 million sq miles (6.5 million km).

PLANT TYPES More than 438,000 recorded.

ANIMAL TYPES More than 250,000 recorded.

CLIMATE Hot and wet.

RAINFALL 3 to 10 feet (1 to 3 m) per year.

Hydrocarbons

Hydrocarbons are materials that are made of just carbon and hydrogen atoms. They are the energy storage molecules in all major kinds of fossil fuel, including coal. Benzene, methane, and paraffin are all hydrocarbons that are used as fuel. Petroleum, or crude oil, is a mixture of several hydrocarbons. When hydrocarbons are mixed with oxygen, or burned, they release carbon dioxide into the air that can contribute to global warming and climate change.

Biogas

Methane is a slightly cleaner fuel than other hydrocarbons. When animal manure and plant materials rot or decay, they produce methane gas, which is also known as a biogas. This can be stored in a tank, and piped to water heaters and stoves.

The methane phantom!

For years, people believed that strange spirits inhabited bogs and marshlands. Often at night, pale and flickering glows of light hovered here and there like phantoms. For a long time no one knew what they were, and local people called them "will-o'-the-wisps."

In fact, these glowing lights are caused by burning methane and other gases, which are produced by rotting plants in the marsh.

Glowing methane gas is often seen rising from bogs and marshes.

In some areas, methane is produced from human waste, collected, and piped to the main buildings to use as fuel.

Acid rain

The burning of fossil fuels sends chemicals into the air that can damage the environment in a different way. These chemicals can turn rain, which all living things depend on, into acid rain.

When we burn fossil fuels in factories or in our cars, for example, chemicals called sulphur and nitrogen are released into the atmosphere. There they mix with water (rain or snow) in the air and become different chemicals, called sulphur dioxide and nitrogen oxides. These can be very harmful to plants and animals, including humans.

Eating into buildings

Acid eats into metal and stone, and it can also damage stained glass and plastics. Buildings are particularly at risk. Those made of types of stone such as limestone and marble contain a mineral called calcite, which is easily damaged by acid rain.

The face of this statue has been dissolved by acid rain.

Lime dosing

Water creatures are very sensitive to the amount of acid in their habitat. Lime-dosing machines automatically check the amount of acid in water. By adding powdered lime to the water, they can reduce the amount of acid if necessary.

Fish die quickly in water that is polluted with acid.

The Acid Rain Program

Around the world, people have worked hard to reduce the pollution that causes acid rain. The Acid Rain Program is an American project that aims to reduce the amount of sulphur dioxide and nitrogen oxides produced by industry, by taking money from those that pollute and giving it to those that don't. The Acid Rain Program has so far proved successful.

Sulphur comes mostly from power stations that make electricity.

PRECIOUS WATER

Human beings are "water creatures." Water makes up 60 percent of our body, 70 percent of our brain and 80 percent of our blood. While we can go almost a month without food, our bodies can't survive one week without water.

Water covers most of the planet, but only a tiny percentage is freshwater, and most of that is ice. Less than 1 percent of all Earth's freshwater is available for human use. Millions of people in the world live on less than 3½ gallons (13 L) a day. One in five doesn't have access to safe drinking water. In the 20th century, the world's population tripled, and it is set to grow even further. Most people will be born in countries that already suffer from water shortages, and the situation will get more serious.

Water in reserve

In many countries, even those that have dry climates, there is water below the ground. It has collected over many years, having seeped through the surface soil and rocks until it hit hard, nonporous rock. Water that has settled on the rock layer, known as the water table, is called groundwater. Groundwater is clean because the soil and porous rock filter out harmful bacteria.

Oxen are used to raise water from a well, which will provide water for humans, animals and crops.

Digging a well

One way of reaching water at the water table is to dig a hole, or well, to reach it. Many people rely on wells to supply water for drinking, irrigation and washing. If groundwater is filled up by rain, the water table is kept at its useful level. But if climate change alters the amount of rain that falls, the water table level is lowered and wells run dry.

The water table

When it rains, much of the rainwater seeps back into the ground, filling up the water table.

rain falls from clouds

POROUS ROCKS

water seeps through porous rocks

water collects on top of nonporous rocks

water from the water table flows into rivers and lakes

NONPOROUS ROCKS

Spreading deserts

In some parts of the world the climate is very dry. Areas with this kind of climate are called deserts. A desert usually has less than 10 inches (25 cm) of rain per year, although in some years there may be no rain at all.

The hottest deserts exist in areas where there are belts of warm, dry, sinking air, or high-pressure zones. These include the Sahara, where temperatures can reach 122°F (50°C) during the day, and the Saudi Arabian Desert. Cold deserts, such as the Gobi Desert, usually exist in the rain shadows of mountains, while mild desert climates are generally found along the west coast of continents.

Drier and drier

Deserts are growing in many parts of the world. Once land is empty of plants, perhaps due to overgrazing by farm animals, the wind can blow the dusty surface away and spread it further.

Once a piece of land is dry, the air above it is drier too, and rainfall is reduced, so the land gets drier still. This process is called "desertification."

Many families in Africa must carry water a long distance to their homes.

A sunflower crop fails through lack of water.

Saving crops

As deserts spread, it's difficult for farmers to keep their crops alive. When crops fail, people and animals may starve. Australian scientists expect their country to suffer from many more droughts in the next 50 years. They are developing new types of wheat that can grow just as well as normal types of wheat – but with much less water.

Dew

Even in the driest areas, there is always some water in the air, in the form of invisible vapor. At night, the air temperature falls and some of the vapor turns back into water in the form of dew. This can be collected around crops.

Draining the sea

The Aral Sea used to be the fourth largest lake in the world. Today, it is mostly desert. It has lost three-quarters of its water since the 1960s, when the rivers that flowed into it were diverted to irrigate crops. The fish died and 60,000 fishermen lost their livelihoods. Lakeside villages were stranded and then deserted. The lake waters used to take in the summer heat and keep the winters mild. Now the weather is far more extreme.

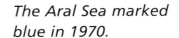

The Aral Sea marked blue in 1970.

The shrinking sea is plain to see by 2008.

Today, boats are stranded several miles from the water's edge.

Migrating birds fly great distances to their original lake habitats.

Migrations

Every winter huge numbers of birds migrate, or fly great distances, to different climates where they can find food. Geese that live on lakes and rivers in Canada and the northern part of the United States, for example, migrate from a cold winter climate to a warmer one. They may cover up to 3,100 miles (5,000 km), returning in the spring to their original habitat.

Shrinking lakes

The Great Lakes on the border of Canada and the United States are among the largest in the world. But they are getting smaller. The shrinking is due to warmer and drier winters. This causes problems, and not only for the migrating birds. In some areas, fish are no longer able to lay their eggs. Shipping is difficult too, for the waters are too shallow for some boats to be used. Dredging the lake bottom causes further problems as old pollutants are released that are damaging the ecosystems.

MELTING ICE

One of the results of climate change is the loss of ice at Earth's poles. As the temperature rises the ice melts and becomes part of the oceans. When ice covering the sea melts, it doesn't affect sea levels: they don't rise because the ice was part of the ocean to begin with. But when ice on land melts, the water or ice breaking from glaciers will cause sea levels to rise.

Penguins huddle on floating ice floes in the Antarctic.

Thin ice

Three-quarters of all the water on Earth is ice. Much of this is located around the North and South Poles, and used to be thick ice that had developed over many centuries. A great deal of this ice has now melted and has been replaced by thinner, one-year ice that forms each winter. This thinner ice melts much more easily during the following summer.

The Arctic ice cracks in the spring thaw.

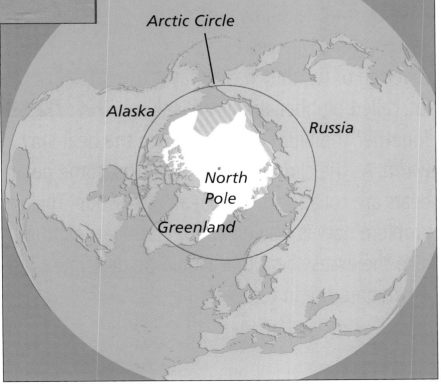

The grey shaded area shows ice sheet that melted in 2009, more than had ever melted in the previous 30 years.

29

Save the polar bear!

As climates change, animal species that rely on those climates to remain the same may become endangered. The polar bear, for example, relies on the Arctic climate to provide the cool temperatures its body needs. The cold also creates the ice on which the polar bear hunts, breeds and sometimes makes its den.

Keeping warm

Over many generations polar bears have evolved to survive in cold temperatures. As well as a thick covering of fur, they have a layer of fat, called blubber, under their skin. Together, the blubber and fur help the bear stay warm. As the climate becomes hotter, some polar bears are collapsing from heat exhaustion. Their problem now is staying cool. Polar bears cannot take the excess heat that would be generated by a 4-degree rise in temperature.

Bears rest on the ice as they move between their feeding grounds.

Rare bear

A warmer climate creates another problem for polar bears. They normally hunt seals during the winter and spring, and then return to shore. They use their store of body fat to survive and to feed their cubs. However, in the Hudson Bay region of Canada, the ice is now melting three weeks earlier: the bears that live there have less time to hunt, so they can't store all the body fat that they need. This means there are fewer bears and fewer cubs being born. Bears are becoming smaller in size too.

A tagged mother with her cub.

Keeping Track

Scientists need to follow the movements of polar bears to find out how they are being affected by warmer temperatures. They do this by fitting female bears with radio collars. A male bear's neck is too big to hold the collar on. The radio feeds a satellite with information on where the bears are at any given time.

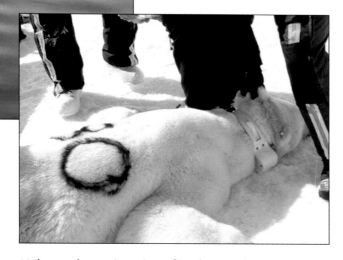

When the scientists fit the radio collars, they also collect information about a bear's health, its weight and its age. The bear can be tracked from the air by its number.

FLOODS

When a river, lake or sea overflows its banks, the result is a flood. In some cases, such as the Nile River in Egypt, the annual flood is a good thing as it brings water to irrigate crops. But often floods bring devastation to areas, wrecking homes and crops and endangering people and livestock. Floods in China and Bangladesh, for example, have been particularly damaging.

Scientists are worried that climate change and global warming are contributing to a rise in the number of floods around the world. Agricultural land in coastal areas could be lost, and in the worst cases whole towns and cities could end up underwater. Predicting sea level rise is very difficult, but many climate scientists forecast a rise in sea level of around 3.3 feet (1 m) by the end of this century – or more if the Greenland and Antarctic ice sheets continue to melt.

This town in Britain suffered major flooding when the river overflowed its banks.

ECOSYSTEMS

An ecosystem is a collection of plants and animals that depend upon each other in order to live. As well as interacting with each other, they also rely on the climate in which they live remaining the same.

If the balance of an ecosystem is disturbed, plants and animals, including people, suffer. Climate change means changes in temperature, rainfall, wind and sunlight, and a change in any of these can bring about disaster. In Mali in Africa, for example, warmer temperatures have caused a drought that has wiped out many plants used for traditional medicine. In the past, the people there had used these to help cope with illnesses.

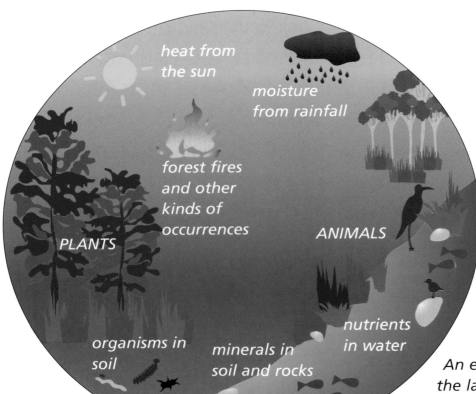

heat from the sun

moisture from rainfall

forest fires and other kinds of occurrences

PLANTS

ANIMALS

organisms in soil

minerals in soil and rocks

nutrients in water

An ecosystem is made up of the land and the atmosphere above it, as well as the living things that live and grow in the area.

In a watery area such as this one, a whole host of plants and animals will find a home. The plants will provide essential food for the animals, while the animals, in turn, will eat and disperse seeds and help the plants to spread over a larger area.

MIGHTY WINDS

Hurricanes, also known as typhoons or cyclones depending on what part of the world they are in, develop near the equator over waters such as the southern Atlantic, eastern Pacific, Caribbean Sea, and Gulf of Mexico. There, heat from the warm seas causes warm, moist air to rise up over the water, creating a low-pressure system, which brings these strong, rotating winds.

Because of the spin of Earth, a hurricane rotates in an counterclockwise direction around a central "eye." The eye is a circular area of calmer weather and lighter winds. Around the eye is the "eyewall," where the strongest winds blow. As the storm moves, it sucks up warm, moist air from above the sea, making it stronger. The moisture is released as heavy rainfall.

When the hurricane hits land its fierce winds and rainfall can cause terrible damage.

More hurricanes

Meteorologists track the development of hurricanes as they move. Many think that the number of hurricanes that occur will increase as climate change pushes up temperatures, creating more unpredictable and stronger weather systems. They believe this is the result of the warming of the oceans caused by the greenhouse effect.

Hurricanes are given names to avoid confusion. National hurricane centers keep official alphabetical lists, and all hurricanes over a certain size are given a name from the list.

This lighthouse must withstand the battering of stormy seas whipped up by gale-force winds.

Hurricane Katrina

In August 2005, the southern coast of the United States was hit by a devastating hurricane. Named Katrina, it caused widespread flooding and left the city of New Orleans in Louisiana 80 percent underwater.

The hurricane winds themselves reached up to 174 miles (280 km) per hour and traveled 118 miles (190 km) from the storm's center. As well as thousands of buildings being destroyed, nearly 2,000 people lost their lives. Katrina was the sixth-strongest Atlantic hurricane ever recorded.

Seen from space, a hurricane appears as a spinning mass of cloud. The eye is seen as a dot in the middle.

FIRES

Each year, forest fires destroy whole ecosystems as well as causing people to evacuate their homes. Often thousands of acres are burned and the land is laid waste for years. Dry weather makes the fires worse and high winds can act like a fan, spreading flames at breakneck speed.

Scientists believe that the increase in forest fires around the world over the past decade may be related to global warming. Some think that the warming of the surface waters of the eastern Pacific by El Niño may result in fires as well as floods in many parts of the world. They believe that the warm air currents rising from the warmer surface waters are becoming stronger with climate change.

Forests store carbon dioxide. When they are burned down this gas is released into the atmosphere. This could warm the climate more and make the fire problem even worse.

HELPING HAND

Climate change may be a big deal and it may be a global problem. But that doesn't mean that each of us can't do something to help. Here are some of the things we can all get involved in that may reduce or help to prevent climate change.

- Walk or bike to school instead of being driven there.
- Recycle food packaging, like glass, paper, and cans.
- Turn your home's heating down one degree.
- Put food waste into a composter instead of the garbage.
- Fill the kettle with only the amount of water you need.
- A quarter of all the water that enters most homes is used to flush the toilet.
- Baths use a lot (take a shower!), and so does brushing your teeth with the tap running.
- Replace standard lightbulbs with energy-saving ones.
- Switch off electrical devices – don't leave them on standby.

Play wells

In many parts of Africa, it can take hours to fetch water from the nearest source. But now wells are being dug to draw water from deep underground and a special "game" helps to bring it to the surface. A pump is attached to a children's merry-go-round, and the village children are encouraged to spin it around as they play. Every hour more than 260 gallons (1,000 L) of water can be raised in this way. Look for information about a charity you can help.

Nature trips

Many young people are taking part in field study outings and getting to know about their environment. Find out about groups near you and make a difference.

Recycling paper

Our waste paper really does get recycled and used in the manufacture of all kinds of different goods. Remember to separate your paper out for special collection.

Carbon fertilizer

After a forest fire, the earth will be rich with carbon from the burnt wood ash. This acts as a fertilizer and within a short time, new buds will start to sprout and grow. Soon the forest floor will be rich with growth again.

Reduce your "carbon footprint"

If you walk or bike to school instead of traveling by car, you will not be using any form of fuel – just your own energy! You will be helping to reduce the amount of fuel consumption on the planet. You will be reducing YOUR "carbon footprint" – the amount of gas emissions for which YOU are responsible.

GLOSSARY

acid rain Rain that has been made acidic by combining with the chemicals that are released into the atmosphere when fossil fuels are burnt.

Amazon River The largest river in the world in terms of volume of water, stretching almost the entire width of South America, from Peru across Brazil.

artificial satellite An object that humans have launched into orbit around Earth.

atmosphere The layer of gases surrounding Earth, or other planets or stars.

atmospheric pressure The pressure caused by the weight of the atmosphere at any point on Earth.

bacteria Tiny single-celled organisms that can cause diseases as well as perform other tasks, such as helping to digest food.

biogas Any gas, including methane, produced by rotting vegetation and animal manure.

blubber A thick layer of fat located under the skin of whales, seals and similar sea mammals.

calcite A mineral found in rocks such as marble and limestone, easily damaged by acid rain.

carbon A chemical element that exists in many forms, including diamond in its pure form, and coal and petroleum in its impure form.

carbon dioxide A gas made up of oxygen and carbon that is essential to the growth of plants, and is a chief greenhouse gas.

coal A form of carbon that is mined and burned as fuel.

desert An area that receives very little rain and where the land is therefore dry.

desertification The process of land becoming desert as a result of overgrazing, the removal of plant growth or lack of water.

drought An extended period of time when there is a severe reduction in rainfall.

ecosystem A community of living things and the habitat they live in, all functioning together as a unit.

El Niño A cycle of climate changes that occurs across the equatorial Pacific Ocean every few years and brings floods, droughts and other weather disturbances in many regions of the world.

Equator An imaginary line around Earth, halfway between the North and South Poles, dividing Earth into the northern hemisphere and the southern hemisphere.

extinction The complete dying-out of a species of animal or plant.

fertilizer Organic or chemical matter added to soil to promote plant growth.

fossil fuel Fuels such as coal and oil that are formed over millions of years by the decomposition of dead plants and animals.

glacier A large mass of ice that moves very slowly, usually down a mountain valley.

global warming An increase in Earth's average temperature large enough to cause climate change.

gravity The force of attraction that pulls everything towards Earth's center.

greenhouse effect The way Earth's atmosphere traps the sun's heat and warms the planet. More heat is trapped as a result of the presence of greenhouse gases, leading to global warming.

greenhouse gas Any gas in Earth's atmosphere that traps heat and contributes to the greenhouse effect, including water vapor, carbon dioxide, methane, nitrous oxide and ozone.

groundwater Water that has collected underground and that appears on the surface in springs and streams.

humidity The amount of moisture trapped as water vapor in the air.

hurricane A rotating storm system of thunderstorms, strong winds and heavy rain. Known as a typhoon in the Pacific.

hydrocarbon An organic compound of carbon and hydrogen often found in petroleum, coal, and methane. It is formed from organic matter that rotted millions of years ago.

hydrogen   A gas making up 75 percent of the mass of our universe. It is the lightest and most abundant chemical element.

ice cap   A mass of ice that covers up to 19,300 sq miles (50,000 sq km).

irrigation   The distribution of water for agriculture.

lime-dosing   The process of checking the acid levels of water and reducing it by the addition of lime.

limestone   A kind of rock composed largely of calcite and widely used in building.

logging   Cutting down certain types of trees for forest management and timber.

marble   A type of limestone formed under great pressure millions of years ago and used for building.

meteorologist   Someone who studies the processes and changes of Earth's atmosphere and attempts to forecast the weather.

methane   A powerful greenhouse gas, formed when organic matter rots.

migration   The regular, seasonal movement of groups of animals.

monsoon   A period of heavy wind and rain in southern Asia, during which the area receives most of its annual rainfall.

nutrient   A substance that provides nourishment for plants and animals.

ocean   A large expanse of sea, in particular the Atlantic, Pacific, Indian, Arctic, and Antarctic; or the entire body of salt water that covers more than 70 percent of Earth's surface.

ocean current   A constant movement of ocean water that is caused by tides, wind, waves, and climate.

orbit   The path that a body in space, such as the moon, takes around another body, such as Earth.

overgrazing   Too many animals feeding on too little vegetation.

oxygen   A gas that is abundant in and around the Earth and is essential to life. It forms about 20 percent of Earth's atmosphere.

ozone layer   A layer in Earth's atmosphere that contains high levels of ozone, a colorless gas. It acts to protect Earth by absorbing around 95 percent of the sun's ultraviolet rays.

permafrost   The name given to frozen soil that stays frozen throughout the year, such as in polar regions.

petroleum   An oily, liquid mixture of hydrocarbons found in Earth's crust and usually extracted by drilling. It is refined or distilled to produce petrol, methane and other oils and fuels.

play well   A playground merry-go-round installed over a well so that children's playing pumps up water for the community.

pollution   The introduction of elements into an environment that harm or upset the ecosystem.

radio collar   A special collar fitted to an animal so that its movements can be tracked.

rainforest   A dense evergreen forest with high rainfall, generally located in tropical regions, and host to large numbers of plant and animal species.

recycling   The processing of used or waste materials to make new products.

temperature   A measure of the hotness or coldness of an object or subject according to a scale.

termite   Ant-like insects that live in colonies of up to several million individuals.

volcano   A mountainous vent in Earth's crust that may erupt, spewing out lava, ashes, and hot gases.

water table   The underground level below which the earth is saturated with water. It is not constant, but changes with weather and water use.

water vapor   Water in its gaseous state.

weather cycle   The typical pattern of weather in a region which changes from season to season.

weather satellite   An artificial satellite that transmits information to meteorologists.

weather station   A center or machine that records the daily weather.

well   A deep hole leading from the surface of the ground to a source of water below, through which water can be raised.

INDEX

PHOTO CREDITS

(t = top, b = bottom, l = left, r = right)

Pg 1 – Jan Martin Will / Shutterstock
Pg 2 – Dainis Derics / Shutterstock
Pg 5 – (t) Ali Ender Birer / Shutterstock, (b) Prokhorov Andrey / Shutterstock
Pg 7 – (l) NASA, (r) Rich Carey / Shutterstock
Pg 9 – Peter Hansen / Shutterstock
Pg 10/11 – NASA
Pg 11 – NASA
Pg 12 –Tim Graham / Alamy
Pg 12/13 – Ecoprint / Shutterstock
Pg 13 – Jim Lopes / Shutterstock
Pg 14 – Styve Reineck / Shutterstock
Pg 15 – (t) Imantsu / Shutterstock, (b) Pixel Memoirs / Shutterstock
Pg 16/17 – Will & Deni Mcintyre / Science Photo Library,
Pg 17 – Guentermanaus / Shutterstock
Pg 18 – RajendraShaw / Panos Pictures
Pg 18/19 – Dustin Mudry / Shutterstock
Pg 20 – Alex Yeung / Shutterstock
Pg 20/21 – Alexey Fateev / Shutterstock
Pg 21 – David Zagorski / Shutterstock
Pg 22/23 –Mana Photo / Shutterstock
Pg 23 – Jeremy Richards / Shutterstock
Pg 24/25 – Frederic Courbet / Panos Pictures
Pg 25 – LianeM / Shutterstock
Pg 26 – gopixgo / Shutterstock
Pg 27 – James F Laurie / Shutterstock
Pg 28 – Armin Rose / Shutterstock
Pg 28/29 – Kkaplin / Shutterstock
Pg 30 – Jan Martin Will / Shutterstock
Pg 31 – (t) Steven Kaziowski / Still Pictures, (b) Dr Bruce G Marcot / www.taos-telecommunity.org
Pg 33 – ronfromyork / Shutterstock
Pg 35 – Perica Dzeko / Shutterstock
Pg 37 – (t) photo bank.kiev.ua / Shutterstock, (b) Luisa Puccini / Shutterstock

Pg 38/39 – NASA
Pg 40/41 – Stephanie Swartz / Shutterstock
Pg 42 – Gideon Mendel / Corbis
Pg 43 – (tl) Marek Pawluczuk / Shutterstock, (tr) Paul Prescott / Shutterstock, (bl) Steven W Moore / Shutterstock, (br) Yan Zenkis / Shutterstock